BIG BOOK OF SMASH HITS 2003

GW00418917

WISE PUBLICATIONS
part of The Music Sales Group
London/New York/Sydney/Paris/Copenhagen/Berlin/Madrid/Tokyo

Published by
Music Sales Limited
8/9 Frith Street, London W1D 3JB, England

Exclusive Distributors:
Music Sales Limited
Distribution Centre, Newmarket Road, Bury St. Edmunds,
Suffolk IP33 3YB, England.
Music Sales Pty Limited
120 Rothschild Avenue
Rosebery, NSW 2018,
Australia.

Order No. AM977515
ISBN 1-84449-091-2
This book © Copyright 2003 by Wise Publications

Music arranged by Derek Jones.
Music processed by Paul Ewers Music Design.
Printed and bound in Malta by Interprint Ltd.

Your Guarantee of Quality
As publishers, we strive to produce every book to the highest
commercial standards. The music has been freshly engraved and
the book has been carefully designed to minimise awkward page
turns and to make playing from it a real pleasure. Particular care
has been given to specifying acid-free, neutral-sized paper made
from pulps which have not been elemental chlorine bleached.
This pulp is from farmed sustainable forests and was produced
with special regard for the environment. Throughout, the printing
and binding have been planned to ensure a sturdy, attractive
publication which should give years of enjoyment. If your copy
fails to meet our high standards, please inform us and we will
gladly replace it.

www.musicsales.com

ALL THE THINGS SHE SAID

Words & Music by Sergei Galoyan, Trevor Horn, Martin Kierszenbaum, Elena Kiper & Valerij Polienko

All the things she said, all the things she said, run-ning through my

head, run-ning through my head, all the things she said. This is not e-nough.

I'm in

se-ri-ous shit, I feel to-tal-ly lost,_ if I'm ask-ing for help_ it's on-ly be-cause_

be - ing with you_ has op - ened my eyes. Could I ev - er be - lieve such a per - fect sur - prise? I keep

ask - ing my - self, won - der - ing how._ I keep clos - ing my eyes, but I can't block you out._ Wan - na

fly to a place_ where it's just you and me,_ no - bo - dy else,_ so we can be free,_

(no - bo - dy else,_ so we can be free.)_ All the things she said, all the things she said, run - ning through my

2. And I'm all mixed up feel - ing corn - ered and rushed. They

say it's my fault, but I want her so much, wan - na fly her a - way where the sun and the rain_ come in

BEAUTIFUL

Words & Music by Linda Perry

(Don't look at me)

Vocal ad lib.

1. Ev - 'ry day__ is so
2. To all your friends you're de -

BE MINE

Words & Music by David Gray & Craig McClune

1. From the ve-ry first mo-ment I saw you, that's when I knew,
(Verse 2 see block lyric)

22

(Bo - dy's on fire, my bo - dy's on fire. My bo - dy's on fire, my bo - dy's on fire. My

bo - dy's on fire and I'm los - ing my sa - ni - ty.)_____ Be mine, be mine.

Repeat to fade

Verse 2:
If I had some influence girl
With the powers that be
I'd have them fire that arrow at you
Like they fired it right t me
And maybe when you're heart and soul are burning
You might see
That everytime I'm talking with you
It's always over too soon
That everyday feels so incomplete
Till you walk into the room
Say the word now girl
I'll jump that moon.

Come on baby it's OK
Rainy, shiny, night or day
There's nothing in the way now
Don't you see, be mine, be mine
Winter, summer, day or night
Centigrade or fahrenheit
Baby till you're heart belongs to me
Be mine, be mine.

BORN TO TRY

Words & Music by Delta Goodrem & Audius Mtawarira

I've learned to love,_____ be un-der-stand-

-ing_____ and be-lieve in life._____ But you got-ta make choi-

-ces,_____ be wrong or right._____ Some-times you got-

-ta sa-cri-fice__ the things_ you like._____ But I was born_____

27

DON'T WORRY

Words & Music by D. Hastings, Natalie Appleton & Craigie Dodds

Don't wor - ry 'cause I'll al - ways be there_____ for you.__

In the hea - vens_____ a - bove.__

Don't wor - ry 'cause I'll al - ways be there_____ for you.__

1.

Al - ways be there.

CLOCKS

Words & Music by Guy Berryman, Jon Buckland, Will Champion & Chris Martin

to be tamed.___ Sing - ing: You___

___   are.___   You___

___   are.___

You___   are.___

38

And no - thing else com - pares.

And no - thing else com - pares.

40

Verse 2:
Confusion that never stops
The closing walls and the ticking clocks
Gonna come back and take you home
I could not stop that you now know, singing:
Come out upon my seas
Cursed missed opportunities
Am I a part of the cure?
Or I am a part of the disease, singing:

You are *etc.*

COME UNDONE

Words & Music by Robbie Williams, Boots Ottestad, Ashley Hamilton & Daniel Pierre

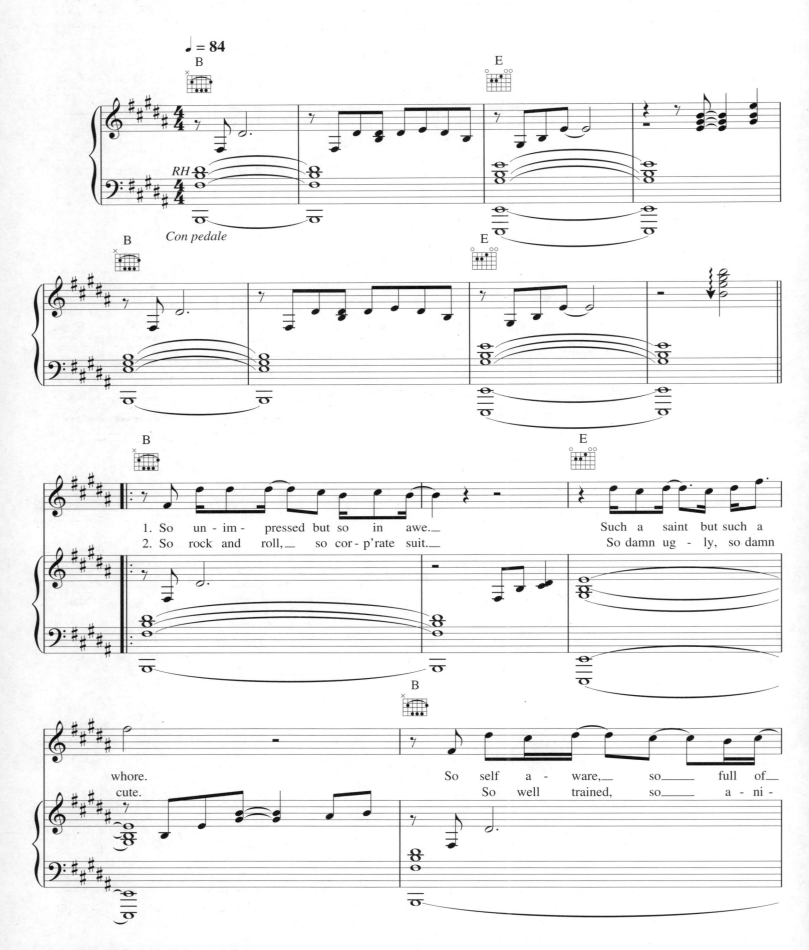

CRY ME A RIVER

Words & Music by Justin Timberlake, Scott Storch & Tim Mosley

HERE IT COMES AGAIN

Words & Music by Marius De Vries, Melanie Chisholm & Robert Howard

I'M GONNA GETCHA GOOD!

Words & Music by Shania Twain & R.J. Lange

D.S. al Coda

Coda

64

Verse 3:
I've already planned it
Here's how it's gonna be
I'm gonna love you
And you're gonna fall in love with me.

So don't try to run. *etc.*

I CAN'T BREAK DOWN

Words & Music by Pete Glenister, Sinead Quinn & Deni Lew

1. Now I know I can han - dle this,_____ I'll close my

68

IF YOU'RE NOT THE ONE

Words & Music by Daniel Bedingfield

can't take it, I___ don't un-der-stand.___ If I'm not made_ for you_ then why___ does my heart tell___ me that I am?___ Is there a-ny way_ that I___ could stay___ in your arms?_____ 2. If

2. And I wish___ that you___ could be___ the_____ one I_____ die___ with.___

74

THE LONG GOODBYE

Words & Music by Paul Brady & Ronan Keating

1. I know they say if you love some-bo-dy you should set them free, (so they
2. Some-times I ask my heart did we__ real-ly give our love a chance? (Just one

82

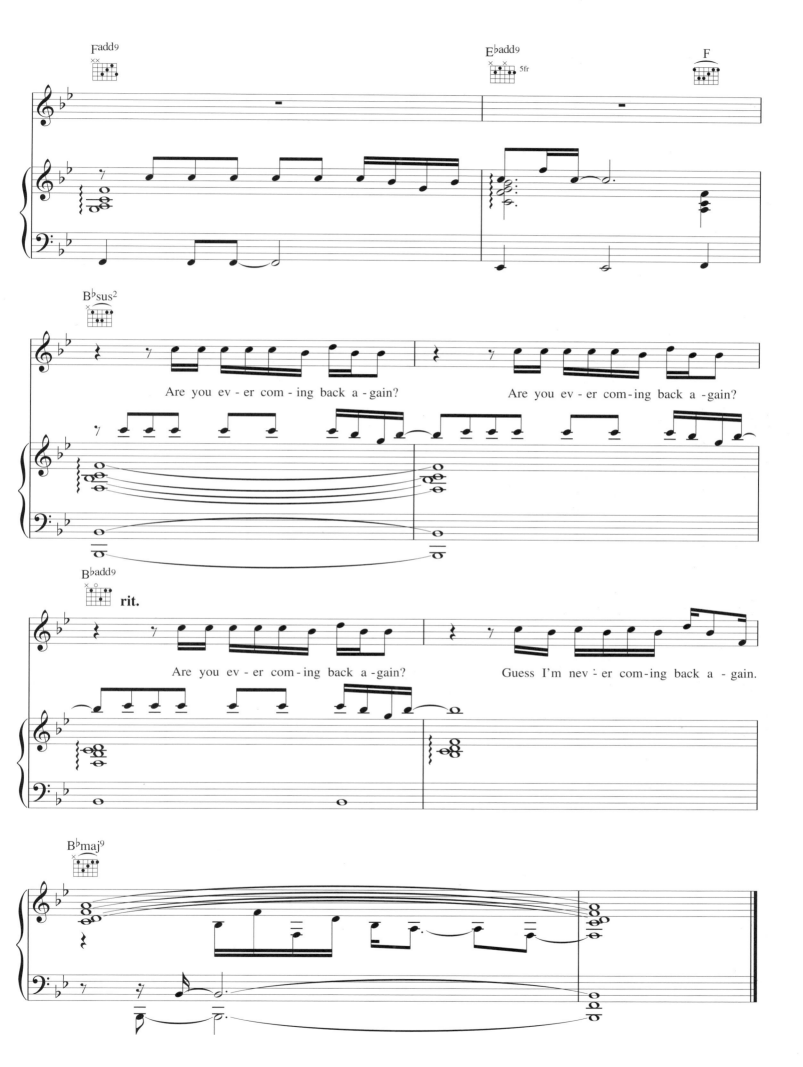

MOVE YOUR FEET

Words & Music by Junior

88

RISE & FALL

Words & Music by Craig David, Sting & Dominic Miller

you think I___ don't care,___ but you don't re-al-ise what this means to me.___

So let___ me have___ just one more___ chance.___ I'm

not the man___ I used___ to___ be.___ Used___ to be.___ Some-times

___ in life___ you feel___ the fight is ov - er and it seems

- er. and it seems_ as though the wri - ting's on_____ the

wall.____ Su - per - star___ you've fin - ally made_ it, but once your pic -

- ture be - comes taint - ed it's what they call_____

the rise and fall.____

SHAPE

Words & Music by Sting, Dominic Miller, Craig Dodds, Kenneth Dodds,
Mutya Buena, Kiesha Buchanan, Heidi Range & Siobhan Donaghy

103

SPIRIT IN THE SKY

Words & Music by Norman Greenbaum

1. When I die   and they lay me to rest____   gon - na go____ to the place____
2. Pre - pare   your - self,   you know it's a   must,   got - ta have a friend   in   Je -
3. Nev - er been a sin - ner,   nev - er   sinned.   I got a friend in   Je -

best.

best.

Oh,_____ set me up with the spi - rit in the sky._
- ing on up__ to the spi - rit in the sky._

D.S. al Coda

Coda

106

STOLE

Words & Music by Dane Deviller, Sean Hosein & Steve Kipner

-ny - more. With his fa - thers nine and a bro - ken fuse. Since he walked through that class -
-ny - more. With his bag - gy pants and his legs in chains. Since he walked through that class -

-room__ door he's all ov - er prime time news.
-room__ door ev - 'ry - bo - dy knows his name.

Ma - ry's got the same size hands as

Ma - ri - lyn Mon - roe. She put her fin - gers in the im - prints at Mann's

Chi - nese Thea - tre Show.__ She could - 've been a mov - ie star, nev - er got the

SONGBIRD

Words & Music by Liam Gallagher

♩ = 132

1. Talk-ing to the song-bird yes-ter-day,_____ flew me to a
(Verse 2 see block lyric, on 𝄋 instrumental ad lib.)

place not far a-way. She's a lit-tle

Verse 2:
A man can never dream these kinds of things
Especially when she came and spread her wings
Whispered in my ear the things I'd like
Then she flew away into the night.

Gonna write a song etc.

TONIGHT

Words & Music by Steve Mac, Wayne Hector & Jörgen Elofsson

1. La - dy I'm so___ tired, if I took it all___ out on you.
2. I don't wan - na act___ like I know that you'll be___ mine for - ev - er though I___ won't wait for - ev - er.

I nev - er meant___ to. If I left you out - side,
Don't want you to feel___ like

so.

So put your best dress___ on,___

wrap your-self___ in___ my arms___ my___ love.___ To-

-night, gon - na make it up,___ to you;___ to - night___ gon - na make love___ to you___ to - night,___

120

U MAKE ME WANNA

Words & Music by John McLaughlin, Steve Robson & Harry Wilkins

1. To start it off, I know you know me. To come to think of it, it was
2. Well I know that these feel-ings won't end now. They get strong-er if I

on-ly last week that I ___ had a dream ___ a - bout us, ___
see you a - gain. Ba - by I'm tired ___ of be -

___ - ing ___ oh. ___ That's why I'm here, I'm
feel the same. friends. ___ I wan-na know if you

writ-ing this song. To tell the truth you know I've been hurt-ing all a - long.
feel the same. And could you tell me do you feel my pain?

Some way let_____ me know_____ you__ want me girl.
Don't_____ leave me in doubt._____

Ev -'ry time you see me, what do you see? I feel like I'm a

poor man__ and you're the Queen. Ooh, ba - by you're the on - ly thing__ that I real - ly need.

Ba - by that's why._____ You